First Day of School

Kelton
I hope you have a
wonderful time at school!
♡ Grandma
Sept. 2016

Library and Archives Canada Cataloguing in Publication

Bantle, Jason Leo, 1972-
First day of school / Jason Leo Bantle, Lori Nunn.

ISBN 978-0-9783406-1-2

1. Grizzly bear--Juvenile literature. 2. Bear cubs--Juvenile
literature. 3. Grizzly bear--Pictorial works--Juvenile literature.
I. Nunn, Lori, 1958- II. Title.

QL737.C27B349 2008   j599.784   C2008-902656-X

2nd Edition Print - February 2011
Text copyright © 2011 Lori Nunn/Jason Leo Bantle
Photography copyright © 2011 Jason Leo Bantle
Ink drawings copyright © 2011 Robyn Wong

Printed in Canada by Friesens Corporation

It's time for your FIRST DAY OF SCHOOL !

You've practised tying your shoelaces 10 times or more.

Pull out the new backpack you squeezed behind the toy box in your bedroom closet.

Stuff it with your favourite lunch, don't forget a juicy red apple.

Everything is ready. Are you?

Now let's have some fun!

Pretend grizzly bear cubs are enjoying their
FIRST DAY OF SCHOOL.

Of course you know bears don't go to school,
but if they did, what do you *think* they'd learn on their
FIRST DAY OF SCHOOL?

Use your imagination . . .

Out in the forest there were three bears, a momma bear and two little bears. The curious little bears agreed going to school might be fun so . . .

One sunny morning momma bear guided the little bears to the edge of the forest. The excited little bears waited in the tall grass. They took turns watching for the bright yellow school bus to come bouncing down the bumpy road.

The yellow school bus stopped at the corner just long enough for the little bears to jump on and find a seat. They waved goodbye to momma bear.

At school the teacher called the little bears to attention. It was going to be a busy day starting with learning how to . . .

SWIM !

"Follow me," said the teacher sliding into the cold water.

Splish splash, splish splash !

With eyes open under the water,
the little bears were snorkelling as they
swam across the lake following right behind their teacher.

Gurgle gurgle, gurgle gurgle !

Going to school was fun, both little bears agreed,
but it was making them . . .

HUNGRY !

Luckily the next lesson the little bears learned was how to **fish** !
"Look," said the teacher pointing to some fish hidden in the weeds.

K-plunk . . . in went one little bear.

Psssssh . . . the other little bear followed.

The little bears stood together eating their catch.

Crunch crunch, crunch crunch !

A fish makes a delicious shared lunch! They both agreed going to school was fun, and with full bellies it was time to learn how to . . .

CLIMB !

"Follow me," said the teacher climbing up onto a wet log.

"Whoops!" One little bear fell down.

Thumpidy,

thump thump . . . .

THUMP !

"I'll show you how to do it," said the teacher as the little bear struggled to climb up. Before long they were both balancing on the slippery log when suddenly . . .

HONK ! HONK ! HONK !

The little bears heard the yellow school bus bouncing down the road.

"Follow me," said the teacher . . .

climbing over logs,

swimming across the lake,
splish splash, splish splash,

         gurgle gurgle, gurgle gurgle,

arriving back at the waiting school bus.

The little bears jumped on the school bus and waved goodbye to their teacher as the bus drove away. The little bears agreed their first day of school had been a fun adventure!

Along the short walk home momma bear asked the little bears what they learned at school. They were excited to share their adventures of swimming, snorkelling, fishing, and climbing.

The three bears arrived home just in time for dinner.
Momma bear had been fishing so . . .

Crunch crunch, crunch crunch !

A fish makes a tasty dish! Going to school was fun, but the little bears were happy to be home with momma bear.

Soon after dinner . . .

"Oooooooooo, yawned one little bear.

"Aaaaaaaaaa," yawned the other. Going to school was fun, but the little bears were ready for . . .

A good night's **SLEEP !**

Life in the Wild for a Grizzly Bear Cub

A mother bear teaches her cubs everything they need to know to survive.

At birth grizzly bear cubs are tiny, blind and toothless. The cubs grow quickly, the first summer they follow mother bear on hunting trips and the second summer they begin hunting on their own.

Mother bear teaches the cubs how to find food over a large area, showing them where to look for insects, leaves, berries, roots, salmon, trout and some mammals. They learn how to fish by watching mother bear and then trying to do what she does.

The cubs learn where, when, and how mother bear dens up for the winter. They learn how to avoid other bears, cougars, wolves and especially people.

Grizzly bear cubs gain a keen sense of smell, they sniff odours from a mile away if the wind is right. Their hearing and vision become as good as yours or mine.

As a grizzly bear cub grows, its big paws, long sharp claws, round flat face and hump on its back show you it is a grizzly bear, not a black bear.